POWER PLAYS:

A KISS FROM FRANCE

Other titles from the Power Plays series:

The Fat of the Land
Under the Hammer   (in preparation)
Raceworld One   (in preparation)
Boycott   (in preparation)

POWER PLAYS: ENGLISH THROUGH DRAMA

Series Editors:
Bill Lucas and Brian Keaney

A KISS FROM FRANCE

Brian Keaney

Stanley Thornes (Publishers) Ltd

First published in 1990 by:
Stanley Thornes (Publishers) Ltd
Old Station Drive
Leckhampton
CHELTENHAM GL53 0DN
England

British Library Cataloguing in Publication Data
Keaney, Brian
   A kiss from France. – (Power plays). –
English through drama
   I. Title II. Series
   822.914

ISBN 0–7487–0501–5

Typeset by 🅵🄰 Tek Art Ltd, Croydon, Surrey.
Printed and bound in Great Britain at The Bath Press, Avon.

CONTENTS

ACKNOWLEDGEMENTS

The author and publishers would like to thank the following for permission to reproduce contemporary photographs and posters:

Imperial War Museum, pp. 43,44,48,49,52.
Mary Evans Picture Library, p.44 (Top).

Also the following for permission to reproduce copyright material:

Age Exchange Theatre Trust, Blackheath, for extracts from *What Did You Do In The War, Mum?*, edited by Pam Schweitzer, Lorraine Hilton and Jane Moss, pp.41,47; B.T. Batsford for statistics on women's employment 1914–18 from *Life in Britain in World War One* by C. Gilchrist, p.61; Faber and Faber Ltd for the extract from *Memoirs of an Infantry Officer* by Siegfried Sassoon, p.55; Victor Gollancz Ltd for extracts from *Chronicle of Youth* by Vera Brittain, edited by Alan Bishop, pp.50–1; Michael Joseph Ltd for extracts from *1914–18: Voices and Images of the Great War* copyright © Lyn Macdonald (1988), pp.45,46,53–4,61,62; Oxford University Press for the extract from *Acquaintances* by Arnold Toynbee (1967), p.57; Penguin Books for the extract from 'A Question of Courage' from *A Long Way To Go* by Marjorie Darke, pp.57–9; Laurence Pollinger Ltd/Estate of Frieda Lawrence Ravagli for the extract from the *Collected Letters* of D.H. Lawrence, published by Penguin Books, p.46; Tressell Publications for the extract from *Contemporary Accounts of World War One*, p.53.

INTRODUCTION

To the teacher and student

This book is designed for use in:

English

Drama

History

Social Studies

It contains a play and a variety of stimulating support material.

There are a number of assignments suitable for GCSE.

It is designed so that it could be used both in the classroom and for individual study.

CHARACTERS

Ted Coleman

Tommy Harris

Dorothy Salmon

Rose Griffiths

Sidney Salmon

Albert Warren

Vera Hammond

Sammy

The action of the play takes place between 1914 and 1917 in East London. Simultaneously we see two soldiers, Tommy Harris and Sidney Salmon, in the trenches in France.

A Kiss From France was originally performed by students of Leicester Polytechnic in schools in the London Borough of Redbridge in 1988. It was devised with the aid of co-directors Carole Pluckrose and Keith Homer.

Prologue: Tableau

The Introit from the Fauré Requiem is playing as the audience enter. The company of actors is seated around the acting area. Two soldiers, Tommy Harris and Sidney Salmon, are positioned in a tableau. Tommy is clearly dead, Sidney stands above. During the song he begins to go through Tommy's pockets; he finds a wallet with photographs, a letter, and also a packet of cigarettes.

A single voice is heard singing.

'Roses are shining in Picardy
In the hush of the silver dew,
Roses are flowering in Picardy
But there's never a Rose like you.
Roses will die in the summertime.
And a Rose may be far apart.
But there's one Rose that dies not in Picardy,
'Tis the Rose that I keep in my heart.'

At the end of the song, the actors set up Scene One.

SCENE 1

Ted Coleman's Workshop

Ted is working. Enter Tommy.

Ted   You took your time.

Tommy   Sorry, Mr. Coleman. You know what that Vera Hammond is like.

Ted   Mrs. Hammond is a very good customer.

Tommy   Doesn't half talk, though.

Ted   Pays on the nail. Which is more than I can say for some of them.

Tommy   I suppose that's the way women are, eh? They have to talk. It's the way God made them.

Ted   It's not just the women who talk. Now come on, there's a pile of work to do. Did you saw up that timber?

Tommy   What, the shelves?

Ted   Yes.

Tommy   As it happens, Mr. Coleman, I didn't.

Ted   Well, why the hell not?

Tommy   I'm leaving.

Ted   You what?

Tommy   I'm leaving. Going off to fight. For me King and Country.

Ted   And what about your apprenticeship?

Tommy I know. I'm sorry.

Ted Oh good! Oh well, that's all right then. I'll just carry on shall I, doing the work of two?

Tommy I *am* sorry.

Ted Yeah.

Tommy It's something I've got to do. I mean, I know I'm leaving you in the lurch.

Ted I'll say you are.

Tommy But what else can I do? Honest to God, Mr Coleman, what else can I do? If you were my age . . .

Ted When I was your age Tommy, I was grateful to be learning a trade.

Tommy I have been grateful. Really I have. But what else can I do? My country needs me.

Ted I'll tell you what else you can do. You can saw that bleeding timber for those shelves. You heard me. Go on. Get on with it. And then you can bugger off. And take your wages. You know where the cash box is.

Tommy I'll just take up till last week's.

Ted You will not. You'll take for every day you've worked.

Tommy Are you sure?

Ted Yes, I'm sure. And you be sure, too. Be sure you know what you're doing.

Tommy I do, Mr Coleman. I know exactly what I'm doing.

Ted Well, it's the first bloody time you have, son. Go on, get cracking.

Tommy You don't mind, then?

Ted Of course I bloody mind. But I can get another apprentice. You're not the only lad who can hold a chisel. Here, don't take it wrong. You've done all right. You've worked hard. If I was your age I expect I'd be off along with you, running down the road as fast as my legs would carry me. All those lads in uniform. It's a fine thing to be a soldier. Go on then, get sawing. And mind you put them tools away properly when you've finished.

(Tommy has gone. Ted looks up after him)

For God's sake keep your head down.

SCENE 2

Dorothy's Shop

Dorothy is counting her stock. Rose rushes in and sits down.

Rose   (*under her breath*) Phew! Thank God for that!

Dorothy   Hello Rose. What are you doing here at this time of day?

Rose   Just escaped for five minutes. Left little Harry with Mrs. Marshall. I can't stay long. You know what she's like. Half blind and three quarters deaf. Harry'll be off down the road before she even knows he's gone. I don't know. I used to long for the time when he'd be walking. Now I wish I could tie him up.

Dorothy   He's a lovely little boy, though.

Rose   Oh yeah, when he's asleep. Just like his father. That was the only time you could trust him.

Dorothy   Rose.

Rose   Yeah?

Dorothy   How long is it since Harold died?

Rose   Five years.

Dorothy   You miss him, don't you?

Rose   Miss him? His dirty great feet up against me in bed, like two icicles. Course I miss him. But there's no point in thinking about it, is there? You just carry on.

Dorothy   No, I realise that. I only asked 'cos . . .

Rose   'Cos your Sid's going off to fight?

Dorothy   Only, he might not come back. Rose, what if he doesn't come back?

Rose   Come on darling, don't think of the worst.

Dorothy   We haven't been married five minutes.

Rose   And it shows.

Dorothy   How do you mean?

Rose   I mean, Dorothy . . . (*Putting on a silly expression*) Oh, Sidney!

Dorothy   I don't act like that.

Rose   That's better.

Dorothy   But really, Rose. I mean, we haven't had any time together. Not to speak of. At least you and Harold had some time.

Rose   Time to get fed up with each other.

Dorothy   You don't mean that.

Rose   No, I don't. Not completely.

Dorothy   It must have been terrible . . . when he had the accident.

Rose   It was.

Dorothy   I'm sorry. I shouldn't talk about it.

Rose   It's all right. Time heals everything. It's just that we had an argument, the night before. You know, like you do. About nothing. I was still angry the next morning. Sulking, I suppose. I sent him off to work with hardly a word. That's what I regret. I wish we'd made it up.

(*Enter Tommy*)

Tommy   Hello, Mrs. Harris, Mrs. Griffiths. Is Sidney about?

Dorothy Here's another one, signed up for king and country.

Rose You and all?

Tommy We're all off together.

Rose Well, mind you take care of yourself.

Tommy We will, don't you worry. We'll look after each other, and give the bloody Huns something to think about into the bargain.

Dorothy He's out the back, sorting out what he's taking with him.

Tommy Right.

(*Tommy rushes upstage towards Sidney. They exchange excited greetings*)

Sidney How do, mate. What did old Coleman say?

Tommy He said it's all right.

Sidney Right then. Six o'clock tomorrow morning. Dover, here we come!

Rose Like little boys, aren't they? Off on a big adventure.

Dorothy Please God bring them back again safe and sound.

Rose Listen Dorothy, I must fly. I only popped in to say if you need a hand with the shop now that Sid's off . . .

Dorothy Oh thanks, Rose. Do you know, I haven't really had time to think about it.

Rose I don't suppose you have. Anyway, the offer's there.

Dorothy As if you haven't got enough to do with little Harry, and full time.

Rose Yeah, well I'm used to it. I reckon us women'll have to stick together now the war is on, don't you? Without the men.

Dorothy I suppose we will.

Rose   I'd better go. I'll see you later.

Dorothy   Ta ta, love.

Rose   (*turning back for a moment*) Without the men, what will we do?

(*Both women laugh. Exit Rose*)

SCENE 3

Dorothy's Living Room

Dorothy is packing Sid's case. Music. 'Somewhere The Sun Is Shining' is playing underneath the following monologue.

Dorothy   One thing I've never understood about men. They like being told what to do. It's true. Of course they'll deny it if you come out and say it, but all the same it's what they're like. Give them their orders and they're off down the road in a line. Now, women are different. Women like to make their own minds up. Well, some of them do. I know I shouldn't say this, but I think I'm going to like having the shop to myself. Sid reckons he runs it, but it's me who runs it really. I always take the trouble to do it right. I make a list of what's needed. Sid, he carries it round in his head. 'Don't need no pencil and paper', he boasts. All the same, he always forgets something. I wonder what I'll miss most? Covering up his mistakes, that's what I'll miss most. Going along afterwards and ordering the things he's left out. I wonder what he's thinking about now?

When he first told me he was signing up I thought to myself, 'How will I manage without him?'. But Rose, she said 'You'll manage twice as well.' It's all very well for her. She's used to living alone. I need someone to look after, someone else's mistakes to cover up. (*She kisses a single rose and places it in the case*) Don't forget your rifle, Sid!

The Station

Albert Warren is on stage. Enter Tommy, Sidney, Dorothy. Music continues from last scene whilst station is set up.

Sidney   Oh, hold on a minute! Get your ticket ready, Tommy.

Albert   It's all right. I don't need to see them.

Sidney   Oh, but you do, Albert. After all, it's an important job, isn't it Tommy?

Tommy   Very important.

Sidney   After all, somebody has to stay at home and check the tickets.

Dorothy   Sid!

(Vera Hammond enters)

Vera   Hello, Mrs. Harris, Sidney, Tommy. I would like to present you with these flowers. Good luck and God speed.

Sidney   Thank you very much, Mrs. Hammond.

Tommy   Yeah, thanks very much.

Vera   We'll all be thinking of you.

(Dorothy and Sidney move away from the others. Meanwhile Rose and Ted have arrived to see the boys off)

Dorothy   Look after yourself, Sid.

Sidney   Don't worry about me.

Dorothy	But I do worry.
Tommy	It'll all be over in a few months, Mrs. Harris.
Sidney	Of course it will.
Dorothy	Sid, I don't know what I'd do if anything happened to you.
Sidney	Nothing's going to happen to me. I'll be home in no time. I'll tell you what. Albert here will look after the women while we're away, won't you Albert? Hey, but Tommy, do you think it's safe, leaving him here? Do you think he might get up to something?
Dorothy	Please Sid, leave him alone.
Sidney	Well, he makes me sick.

(*'Pack Up Your Troubles' fades in underneath*)

Dorothy	Live and let live.
Sidney	Not any more, Dorothy. That just doesn't hold good any more. He should be joining up with the rest of us.
Tommy	I can see the train. We'd better move up the platform.
Sidney	Hold on a minute, mate.

(*Sidney and Dorothy embrace*)

Sidney	I'll have to go. I'll miss the train.
Dorothy	I love you, Sidney.
Sidney	I love you too.
Dorothy	Write to me. Promise you'll write.
Sidney	Of course I will. You wait. Soon as I get over there, I'll send you a kiss from France.

(*Sid and Tommy exit. Everyone waves them off. Dorothy turns away, pauses for a moment and runs off. Rose goes to her. Exit everyone, leaving Albert counting tickets, and Vera*)

Vera Well, Mr. Warren, it's a pity that everyone doesn't feel the same sense of duty.

Albert I beg your pardon.

Vera That's where you should be, getting on the train with them.

Albert I'll bear that in mind, Mrs. Hammond.

Vera Yes, why don't you?

(*Exit Vera*)

SCENE 5

Vera at home: Tableau

The two soliders take up their positions. Sidney looks at a letter from Tommy's wallet, lights and smokes a cigarette. Vera enters after tableau is set.

Vera 'My Dearest Philip,
It hardly seems possible that a year has passed since the outbreak of war, but already the roses by the front gate are in their second bloom. I wish you could see them. I was talking to the vicar yesterday. He told me that he had heard from a soldier the most remarkable account of something that happened at Mons! It seems that a battalion of our boys were hard pressed by the Germans. Shells were exploding on either side, they knew that they could hold out no longer. Despairingly, one of them called out 'St. George of England, come to our aid!' Suddenly, the air was thick with shapes; the shadowy figures of archers. The air rang with their voices as they called out together 'England, home and duty!' In an instant the Germans were running for their very lives.

I know it must be hard for you, my beloved, seeing no quick end to this war. But remember, darling, that I am proud of you; proud that my husband is an officer in the army of the king, and proud to know, above all, that he is serving the cause of justice.'

(Vera stands for a moment, then exits. Sidney stubs out the cigarette in his helmet, then he and Tommy go back to their seats)

SCENE 6

Home on leave: Ted's Workshop

Ted is measuring a plank of wood.

Ted   Oh, for God's sake. Sammy! Sammy!

(*Enter Sammy*)

Sammy   Yes, Mr. Coleman?

Ted   Can you count, lad?

Sammy   Count, Mr. Coleman?

Ted   (*mimicking him*) Count, Mr. Coleman? Look. This is a rule. See? These little lines on it represent feet and inches.

Sammy   I know that.

Ted   Oh, you do? Well, why the hell don't you use it? Three feet seven inches those shelves are supposed to be. There's not one of them longer than three feet five.

Sammy   Are you sure? (*Tries measuring them himself*)

Ted   Am I sure? I suppose I've been a joiner for the last twenty-five years and I don't know how to measure a plank of wood. These shelves should be three feet seven. Well, they're not. They're two inches short. Now perhaps you'd like to explain that to Mrs. Salmon.

Sammy   She might not notice.

Ted   Pigs might fly!

Sammy   I'm sorry, Mr. Coleman.

Ted   *You're* sorry.

Sammy   What shall we do?

Ted   What shall we do? Start again, that's what. And get a move on. She wants those shelves up before her husband comes back.

(*Enter Vera*)

Vera   Good afternoon, Mr. Coleman.

Ted   Good afternoon, Mrs. Hammond.

Vera   How's Madge?

Ted   She's looking a bit better today.

Vera   Has the doctor been in yet?

Ted   Oh yes. He was in this morning. He's very good.

Vera   Did he say how long before she'd be up and about again?

Ted   Not really.

Vera   Well, a good rest is what she needs.

Ted   That's for certain. She's worn out, you know.

Vera   Illness takes all your strength. You don't have to tell me.

Ted   She slept right through this morning.

Vera   That's the best medicine.

Ted   I just wish she'd sleep at night, though.

Vera   And how's young Samuel settling in?

Ted   Oh, marvellous. First of all I'm teaching him to count. After that we might go on to more difficult things, like learning to tell his left hand from his right.

Vera   Oh, dear, has he been putting a foot wrong?

Ted   You could say that.

Vera   That will never do, Sammy.

Sammy   No, Mrs. Hammond.

Ted   Go on then, get busy with that saw. You've got all those shelves to make for Mrs. Salmon. They won't make themselves.

Vera   She's been busy, hasn't she?

Ted   Dorothy Salmon?

Vera   She's turning the shop upside down, re-arranging everything.

Ted   Wants to have it nice for her husband when he comes back on leave, that's what she said.

Vera   It's this week he's due back, isn't it?

Ted   Yes, first time she'll have seen him in eight months.

Vera   It'll be nice to see the young men coming back in uniform.

Ted   Did you want something special, Mrs Hammond?

Vera   Oh, yes. I just wondered if you could come and have a look at my window frame. It's all rotted away. There's a bit of guttering that's been dripping onto it. I only discovered it the other day. It must have been like that for ever such a long time.

Ted   Will next week be all right?

Vera   Oh, I should think so. Another few days won't make much difference.

Ted   I'll be over first thing on Monday morning.

Vera   That's lovely, Mr. Coleman. Thank you very much. Goodbye.

(Exit Vera then Ted. Enter Sammy. He realises Ted is out the back)

Sammy (*imitating Ted*) Next week be all right for you, Mrs. Hammond? Or shall I do it right away? Perhaps you'd like me to kiss your backside while I'm at it. Perhaps you'd . . .

(Tommy and Sid enter. Seeing Sammy, they creep up behind him)

Sidney Well, if it isn't young Samuel. What are you doing here?

Sammy Hello Sidney. Hello Tommy.

Sidney Where's old Ted?

Sammy He's out the back. Shall I go and get him?

Tommy Yeah. Go and drag the old bugger out here.

Sammy Mr. Coleman! (*He exits*)

(They both sit down. Sidney picks up the piece of wood from the table)

Tommy God! I've missed the smell of this place. Sawdust and old varnish.

Sidney And old Ted's feet, eh?

Tommy Ssh! Here he is.

(Ted enters. Looks from man to man, moves over and shakes Tommy's hand)

Ted Well, well, well. Look what the cat dragged in.

Tommy Hello, Mr. Coleman.

Sidney How do.

Ted Sit yourselves down, lads.

Sidney We musn't stop. Just thought we'd pop in. Haven't even seen me missus yet.

Ted Well, we musn't hold you up from that.

Tommy   How's business?

Ted   Same as always. Too much to do. No time to do it in.

Tommy   How are you managing on your own?

Ted   On my own? I'm not on my own. Although I might as well be. I've got young Sammy here helping me.

Tommy   You mean he's got my job?

Ted   That's right. Meet my new apprentice. Cack-handed Sam.

Sidney   Listen, why don't you come out for a drink with us tonight, Mr. Coleman? You can even bring young Sammy there, if they'll serve him.

Ted   Thanks very much, Sidney. I would, too. But it's Madge. She's not too well.

Tommy   Madge? What's the matter with her, then? Nothing serious, is it?

Ted   Serious enough. Had a bit of a stroke.

Tommy   I'm sorry to hear that.

Sidney   Yeah. That's dreadful.

Ted   Only a small one. Still, bad enough.

Tommy   Is she upstairs?

Ted   Yeah, but she's asleep now. Best leave her.

Sidney   Dot never said.

Ted   Probably didn't want to worry you.

Sidney   Yeah, well I'm sorry. Still, perhaps you'll be able to come out some time.

Ted   I'll try. How long are you back for?

Tommy   Six and a half days.

Sidney	I've got to go.
Tommy	I'll come with you.
Sidney	Check up on that missus of mine. See she's running the shop properly.
Ted	Oh, she's doing that all right. Regular hive of industry it is in there. Got me making shelves for her right left and centre.
Sidney	Making shelves?
Ted	Oh, me and my mouth. I wasn't supposed to let on. She wanted it to be a surprise. Doing the place up for when you came back.
Sidney	Doing it up?
Ted	Her and Rose Griffiths. Been working like Trojans in there.
Sidney	Oh, Rose Griffiths. I might have known she'd be involved.
Tommy	They've done a good job, so I've heard.
Sidney	Well, I shall have to see for myself. Mind you, that Rose Griffiths gets her nose stuck into everything. A woman without a man spells trouble.
Ted	Someone should find her a new husband, if you ask me.
Tommy	A job for Sam. Cack-handed Sam and nosy Rosie. They'd make a lovely couple.
Sidney	Come on, Tommy. I want to see what they've been doing to my shop while I've been serving his majesty. Goodbye.
Tommy	Goodbye, Mr. Coleman.
Ted	Goodbye, lads. Listen, tell Dorothy I'll send Sam around later with the shelves.
Sidney	I shouldn't bother, Mr. Coleman. I've a feeling me and Dorothy might take the evening off work.

Ted   Come on, we'll have none of that talk in here.

Sidney   See you later.

Tommy   Yes. 'Bye.

(*Sid and Tommy exit. Ted picks up his ruler and his coat, and then notices that Sammy has left his tool box*)

Ted   Sammy! Sammy! You've gone and left your . . .

(*He sighs, picks up Sammy's tool box and exits*)

Rose's Rooms

Rose   My mother gave me this ring just before she died. 'Look
after it Rose,' she said, 'it's old gold.' Old tut! The
pawnbroker took one look at it and laughed. 'I wouldn't
give you sixpence for it, Mrs. Griffiths', he told me, 'not
even sixpence.' Well, that's it. Now there's nothing left to
pawn. Last month my wedding ring went. Harry saved up
a whole year to buy that. Before that it was a couple of
silver spoons that had been handed down to me.
Everything I ever had, and that's precious little, pawned.
And I'm no better off at the end of it. I can't raise another
farthing. I've borrowed off Dorothy. I can't ask her for
any more. When her Sid was home on leave a couple of
months ago, he was giving me dirty looks every time he
saw me. I know what he was thinking. 'Here she comes,
on the scrounge again.' Well, I've reached the end of the
road now, at any rate. That's it.

SCENE 8

Dorothy's Shop

Dorothy is packing groceries. Enter Vera.

Vera   Good morning, Dorothy.

Dorothy   Morning, Mrs. Hammond.

Vera   Keeping busy I see.

Dorothy   Doing my best.

Vera   That's what I like to hear.

Dorothy   Any news of Mrs. Coleman?

Vera   They say she's as well as can be expected. I don't think she'll ever get over it properly.

Dorothy   Poor old Ted will have his work cut out now.

Vera   It's my belief that she'll be bedridden for the rest of her days.

Dorothy   Don't say that. We'll keep our fingers crossed.

Vera   She did so much, as well. I was counting on her to help me with Lady Sheldon's war collection. It was just the sort of thing she would have thrown herself into.

Dorothy   Lady what-did-you-say?

Vera   Lady Sheldon's collection. You know, for the boys at the front. Blankets, gloves, woollens of all kinds. Comforts for the troops.

Dorothy   Sounds like a great idea. This Lady Sheldon, she's organising it, is she?

Vera   Well, at a national level. But locally we're looking for volunteers. Of course, I'm giving it as much time as I can. But what it really needs is someone well-known.

Dorothy   But you're very well-known, Mrs. Hammond.

Vera   Yes, but I mean, well-known in the town, to everyone. What I'm trying to say is, you see, I don't mix socially with as many people as Mrs. Coleman or you do.

Dorothy   I think I know what you mean, Mrs. Hammond.

Vera   And with your Sidney going off to war . . .

Dorothy   And me being a tradeswoman.

Vera   Well, I didn't mean anything like that, I assure you.

Dorothy   No, I'm sure you didn't, Mrs. Hammond. But to tell you the truth, I'm so busy at the moment I don't know whether I'm coming or going.

Vera   But you will bear it in mind?

Dorothy   Yes, I'll do that.

Vera   The war's not just abroad: that's what Lady Sheldon says. The women of Britain must learn to fight the war at home.

Dorothy   I couldn't agree more. Right now I'm fighting my war in this shop. So if you'll excuse me, I've got work to get on with, unless there was anything else?

Vera   Well, there was one thing.

Dorothy   Oh, yes?

Vera   I was wondering about my order.

Dorothy   Did you want to change it?

Vera   Not really. It suits me best as it is.

Dorothy   Good.

Vera   I just thought that, with your husband being gone . . . well, you know I always have it delivered.

Dorothy   First thing Monday morning.

Vera   Well, I just thought it might be rather a lot to carry.

Dorothy   That's very thoughtful of you, Mrs. Hammond, but you needn't worry. It's all taken care of. I've got some help, thanks.

Vera   Oh, have you? Well, that's quick work.

Dorothy   Got to keep the business running.

Vera   Quite right. I'm glad. (*She pauses, but cannot resist*) Anyone I know?

Dorothy   Albert Warren.

Vera   Albert Warren!

Dorothy   That's right.

Vera   Oh dear!

Dorothy   Is something wrong?

Vera   Well, I'm just rather surprised, that's all.

Dorothy   At me employing Albert?

Vera   To be quite frank, Mrs. Salmon, I'm surprised you're prepared to allow him in the shop, what with your husband going off to fight for his country. Whatever will he think of it?

Dorothy   Whatever he thinks, Mrs. Hammond, I expect he'll tell me in no uncertain terms, if I know my Sid.

Vera   Well, I suppose you know what's best in your own affairs.

Dorothy   I suppose I do.

Vera	I'm afraid I don't take too kindly to the idea of Albert Warren delivering my groceries.
Dorothy	I'm sorry about that, Mrs. Hammond.
Vera	Yes. Well, I may have to think hard about my order.
Dorothy	Right then, Mrs. Hammond. You do that. I'll tell Albert not to deliver anything until we hear from you.
Vera	Good morning, Mrs. Salmon.
Dorothy	Good morning, Mrs. Hammond.

(*Exit Vera*)

Dorothy	The cheek of that woman. (*She kicks the box of groceries*)

(*Enter Rose*)

Dorothy	Oh, hello Rose. (*She looks for a moment at Rose who is upset*) Is there something the matter? What's wrong?

(*Rose hands her a letter*)

	What's this? (*She begins reading the letter*) What does all this mean? I don't understand all these words. Is this an eviction notice? Is it? Oh Rose, I don't believe it. I told you to come and see me. I could have lent you some money.
Rose	It's three months rent, Dorothy. I owe three months. You couldn't lend me that much.
Dorothy	Three months! But how did it get that bad?
Rose	You know what it's like. I just kept putting it off. I kept putting it off. I kept trying to find the money every week. Every week it just went. This morning I got handed this.
Dorothy	Couldn't you offer to pay a bit of it? I could lend you some. You could pawn something.
Rose	There's nothing left to pawn. It's all in hock already. And I can't borrow what I can't pay back, can I?

Dorothy   You could ask for a bit more time.

Rose   I have done. I went round to the agent's first thing this morning. Not a chance. He wasn't interested. The landlord wants me out and that's all there is to it.

Dorothy   (*she pauses*) Then you'll have to move in with me.

Rose   (*pause*) I was hoping you'd say that.

Dorothy   Well, I wouldn't be much of a friend if I didn't, would I?

Rose   But what will Sid say?

Dorothy   Sid's not here, is he? And I could do with a bit of company.

Rose   But when he comes back?

Dorothy   You might have found somewhere else by then. Anyway, I don't know what you're arguing for. It's not as if you've got much choice, is it?

Rose   No, it isn't. Thanks Dorothy.

Dorothy   It'll be fun. Like when I was a little girl, having a friend to stay. I expect we'll get up to some right larks.

SCENE 9

Ted's Workshop

Ted enters slowly and sits down on his chair. He looks visibly older. Albert stands apart and addresses the audience.

Albert   Can you see what this is? A white feather. Cowardice, that means. If you get a white feather you're a coward. I don't think I'm a coward. I'm just in no hurry to kill anyone, that's all. Would you be? Would you want to go rushing to meet death, shake it by the hand? For what? For honour, glory, for your country? I love my country. I love being free. But most of all, I love being alive. What happens when you're dead? Nobody knows. Nobody wants to find out, either. Not if they've got any sense, anyway. Look at him. His wife's just died. Doesn't know what to do with himself.

(Enter Dorothy. She puts her hands on Ted's shoulders)

Dorothy   I'm sorry to hear about Madge.

(Enter Vera. Enter Rose from elsewhere. They exchange a frosty look. Vera moves towards Ted)

Albert   She's the one who gave it to me. And like a fool I took it. I'm so bloody used to taking railway tickets from people, I just put my hand out and took it from her. Then off she went with her nose stuck in the air.

Vera   I'm so sorry to hear about your wife, Mr. Coleman.

Rose   I'm sorry about Mrs. Coleman.

Albert   I'd better do my bit now. I am sorry, though. I'm sorry for poor old Ted, and I'm sorry for all the rest of us. The old world is passing away. And I'm not sure I like the look of the new one.

(*Albert walks over to Ted, shakes him by the hand and exits. Then Ted exits*)

Dorothy's Shop: Tableau

Dorothy is reading at the table. Sid is soon to take leave of Tommy. He holds him in his arms and kisses his forehead.

(Enter Rose)

Dorothy   Here she is, our very own suffragette. How'd it go, Rose?

Rose   Very well. But where's little Harry?

Dorothy   He's out the back, don't worry. Albert's looking after him.

Rose   Albert!

Dorothy   Don't laugh. He's doing a great job. He's gone round to see Ted Coleman, got all these little wooden off-cuts, and he's been playing with Harry all morning, building houses. I don't know who's the happiest. So go on, tell us, what was it like?

Rose   It was lovely. It was like coming home. That Mrs. Pankhurst isn't at all like they make her out to be. You'd think she was a right dragon from what people say, but she was nice as pie to me.

Dorothy   Can she do anything to help?

Rose   I reckon she can. Or at least she's going to give me a chance to help myself. She's giving me work.

Dorothy   Work?

Rose   She's got this toy factory set up. It's all women working there, just like me. I'm starting right away.

Dorothy   That's marvellous.

Rose   I know I won't be able to help in the shop, but you've done most of the rearranging now, and you've got Albert.

Dorothy   Of course I have. Don't worry about it.

Rose   And I'll be able to give you some money now.

Dorothy   You'd better earn it first. Listen, what's going to happen about Harry? What with the shop and everything I can't . . .

Rose   It's all right. I'm not expecting you to look after him. Or even Albert. She's got that all worked out. There's arrangements made to look after the children. We all take it in turns.

(*Enter Albert with a letter for each of them*)

Albert   Dorothy, here's the letter you've been waiting for.

Dorothy   (*grabbing the letter from Albert*) Oh, it's from Sid. It's from Sid!

Albert   One for you too, Rose.

Rose   Thanks very much.

(*Exit Albert*)

Dorothy   I can hardly bear to open it.

Rose   Go on, for God's sake.

Dorothy   What's yours?

Rose   It'll keep. Come on, open Sid's letter.

(*Dorothy tears open the letter and reads*)

Dorothy   'My darling Dorothy, I'm sorry. I know I said I'd write regularly. But I never was much good at letters. You always used to do the necessary. Anyway, here it is at last. We haven't seen much action yet. Done a lot of marching. Heard some stories about what it's like up the front. Apart from that all we've done is hang about. They're a good bunch of lads, though. Tommy's here and we look out for each other. There's a rumour that we'll be off to somewhere called . . .' (*she breaks off*) How do you pronounce that? . . . Yip or something?

Rose Ypres, I think.

Dorothy '. . . Ypres, before the end of the week. We'll see a bit of fighting then, I should think. I'm keeping my fingers crossed I might get home on leave for Christmas. I've got to go now. We've got manoeuvres for the next few days. Right waste of time that is and all. I never was much of a romantic. You remember when I asked you to marry me? I made a proper mess of it. But I love you, Dorothy, I really do. And I miss you like anything. I'm thinking of you every day, and every night. Look after yourself. Give my regards to old Ted and keep that Rose in her place. All my love, Sid.'

Rose I'll leave you on your own for a bit.

Dorothy No, it's all right. I'll be over it in a minute.

(*She re-reads the letter silently and then deliberately puts it away*)

Dorothy What's yours then?

Rose Oh, nothing that won't keep.

Dorothy Go on, open it. It might be your long lost uncle leaving you a fortune.

Rose Pity I haven't got an uncle. I know who it's from. I'll open it anyway. (*Tears open the letter*) It's from a friend of mine who works as a solicitor's clerk. I just asked him if he could find out who my landlord was. Forgotten I'd asked. No good to me now, anyway. Still, it was worth a try. (*She reads the letter*) Well, I'll be damned. Here, listen to this. 'Dear Rose, sorry it's taken me so long to find the information you wanted. These people are never keen to let you know their business, but I finally found out anyway, more by luck than anything else. Your landlady is quite a famous figure. You've probably heard of her: Lady Sheldon.'

Dorothy   Not *the* Lady Sheldon?

Rose   There can't be two.

Dorothy   And she has the cheek to say 'The women of Britain must learn to fight the war at home'!

Rose   And I always thought it was the Germans who were the enemy.

Dorothy   Doesn't it go to show?

Rose   Just wait till I see that Vera Hammond. 'The war's not just abroad, you know.' Too bleeding right!

The Train: Tableau

The Kyrie from Fauré's Requiem fades in and plays throughout the scene. Sid fastens Tommy's jacket, places his helmet on his chest. Standing back, he looks for a moment at his dead friend.

Sidney   The bombardment started at dawn, and it was sheer hell. Shells, trench-mortars, the lot. You wouldn't believe the noise. It just went on and on. And the same from them. Then we got the order to go over the top. I've never been so scared in me life. But over we went and across the bloody ground. I saw men being cut down all over the place. But me and Tommy were through into one of the trenches. We jumped down and ran along. They were nearly all dead in there. Most of them had lost their limbs. Then we ran into one who was still alive. He was just standing there, looking at us. We didn't think. Butchered him with our bayonets. Tommy and me both. We didn't care. We didn't stop. We had to move on, up and out of the trench again. We ran into some machine-gun fire and had to fall flat on the ground. Suddenly Tommy caught fire as he lay there next to me. A bullet had hit his ammunition belt. I could hear the strike of the gun about a foot above my head. I couldn't move or I'd be ripped to shreds. Tommy was writhing about, trying to put the fire out. Then he began to go off like a firework. The fire was exploding the cartridges in his belt. I just lay there and watched him. It was the most horrible thing I've ever seen. When the machine gun stopped I just turned and ran, back the way I'd come.

SCENE 12

The Town Hall

Rose is painting a 'Welcome Home' poster. Albert and Dorothy are helping to prepare the room. Vera is instructing them. Band music is playing.

Vera   Just a little bigger, I think, Mrs. Griffiths. Does that look right to you, Mrs Griffiths? Mrs Griffiths? (*Rose ignores her*) Mrs Griffiths, I have explained to you that I had no idea that Lady Sheldon was your landlady, And even if I had, there was absolutely nothing I could do. Now was there? Oh well, if you insist. We'll have to assume it's big enough. But really, I think at a time like this we ladies should be sticking together, not quarrelling amongst ourselves. Now I think we should bring in the food from the kitchen.

(*Enter Ted*)

Dorothy   Ted! You've decided to help us out after all.

Vera   Mr. Coleman, how lovely to see you. I was only saying to Mrs. Salmon five minutes ago that it would do you the world of good to get out of that workshop of yours for a change. You've been stuck in there ever since . . . ever such a long time.

Dorothy   I'm glad you could come. There's such a lot to do.

Ted   I only came with some news.

Dorothy   News?

Ted   Tommy's mother got a letter. Just arrived.

Vera   Is he hurt?

Ted   He's been killed.

(He turns away. There is a long silence as they all take in this news. Quietly, without being seen for a moment, Sidney enters)

Sidney   Dorothy.

(They embrace. The scene dissolves, leaving two of the chairs for the next scene)

SCENE 13

Dorothy and Sidney's Parlour

Sid is sitting in a chair, staring vacantly.

Dorothy Sidney, I wonder if you'd do a job for me? Just a little one. I just need to re-stock some of the shelves. There's a load of tins out the back. They're too heavy for me. Would you do that, Sidney? Come on now darling, you've been sitting here ever since you got up. I would ask Albert but he said he'd keep away while you're on leave. He doesn't want to interfere. It'd do you good to get up, Sid. Please Sidney, for me.

(The Kyrie from Faurés Requiem fades in underneath)

Sidney The bombardment started around dawn.

Dorothy Oh, please Sidney, don't start on that again.

Sidney It was sheer hell. Shells, trench-mortars, the lot.

Dorothy Why don't you do something to take your mind off it? Listen, we could shut up shop altogether. Go for a walk. That'd be nice, wouldn't it? We could even take a picnic somewhere. What do you say to that? Come on Sid, talk to me. Let's go for a picnic, eh? Just you and me. Like we used to. Do you remember when we were courting? We used to walk for hours, leave the city behind, get right away from the smoke and houses, and talk about what our life was going to be like together. Come on Sid, let's go for a picnic.

Sidney Then we got the order to go over the top. I've never been so scared in me life. But over we went and across the bloody ground. *(The music swells)*

(Music dissolves into Elgar's Pomp and Circumstance March No. 1, 'Land of Hope and Glory'). Tommy stands up and moves centre stage)

Tommy   You'd have gone to war, don't tell me you wouldn't. Of course you'd have gone. Or would you rather have watched an enemy walk into this country and take over, push your family around? I don't think so. You'd have been off down the road with your mates, like everyone else. And when your boots let in water and there was no ammunition for your rifle; when your orders didn't make any sense and your mates got their stomachs blown away, you'd have looked around you and seen men falling across the face of the earth like ants, and death stamping it's foot on them, and then you'd have said to yourself, 'So this is what it's like to be a hero!'

(Music swells. Tommy stands looking at the audience for a few moments, then returns to his position in the tableau. The single voice comes in with 'Roses of Picardy', as at the beginning of the play, and the actors take their positions around Dorothy and Sidney, as in a photograph)

THE BACKGROUND

Key Events in World War One

1914	August	War declared between Britain and Germany.
	September	Battle of the Marne in France: an early success for the Allies.
1915	January	Trench warfare begins. Each side digs a 400 mile long trench along the border between France and Germany.
	March	Women wishing to work are asked to register their names.
	May	First Zeppelin raid on London.
		Passenger ship 'The Lusitania' is sunk by the Germans.
		Ministry of Munitions formed.
1916	February	First women bus and tram conductresses go to work — known as 'clippies'.
	May	Conscription introduced.
	July	British launch attack on the Germans on the River Somme.
	December	All bread to be made to government specifications.
1917	February	Germans declare all-out war at sea.
	March	Revolution in Russia.
	April	America joins war to help Allies.
		Meat rationing starts.
	May	Germany begins aeroplane raids on Britain.
	June	Bad daylight bombing raids on London.
	November	First British mass tank attack in Cambrai, Belgium.
	December	Peace talks between Germany and Russia.
1918	February	Women over 30 given the vote.
		Rationing extended to basic foods.
	March	Germans launch new offensive on the Western Front.
	August/ September	Allies win Battle of the River Somme and break through the Hindenberg line.
	October	German fleet mutinies and the Kaiser abdicates.
	November	Germany accepts the Allies' terms for an end to the war. An armistice is declared.

Changing Roles for Women

Read Before 1914, the Women's Suffrage movement had been gaining ground. In 1910 the government had been persuaded to set up a Conciliation Committee to draw up a bill to give votes to women.

Mrs Pankhurst called off the militant protests she and others had been making. Although the bill reached its second reading in the House of Commons, it was not allocated enough time to become law.

In 1911, suffragettes caused thousands of pounds worth of damage in London as their anger at the continuing delay spilled over. Post-boxes, empty houses and railway stations were all targets for home-made bombs. In the three years before war started, many women were imprisoned. Some continued their protests by going on hunger-strike.

When war was declared in August 1914, it created an emergency which to most women seemed more important than their own struggle to gain the vote. Most women turned their efforts to working for the war effort, although a sizeable minority resisted this pressure and opposed all forms of fighting and war work.

Because of the large numbers of men leaving the country to fight in France — over a million by the end of 1915 — women found themselves playing a variety of unfamiliar roles at home.

Talk

1 What are the occupations of the women in *A Kiss From France* at the start of the play? Describe your impressions of each of these three characters in as much detail as possible.

2 At the start of the play, which of them do you think would be likely to support the campaign for women's votes? Explain your choice.

Women and Work

Read

There weren't the jobs for women before the war like there have been since. No, a woman was expected to stay at home. Employers wouldn't employ married women, because of the break in having children. My husband said to me, "The day you go to work, I'll pack up. If I couldn't afford to keep you, then I shouldn't have married you."

In the First World War I couldn't go out to work, because I had a baby of two and a half. My husband was working in an army factory. He was only getting 26 shillings a week, and he was supposed to send some to me, but I never received it, so I had to do something desperate. I could have got a job in the Arsenal, but I would have had to do night work. I wanted my mother to look after my baby so I could go to work, but she refused. She couldn't take on the responsibility of having the baby with the bombing going on. So that stopped that.

Ruth Granville

Talk　　*1*　What would you have done if you were Ruth and your husband had gone away to work and left you with a baby and not enough to live on?

　　　　2　Which of the female characters in the play suffers most financial hardship?

　　　　3　In what way is her situation different from Ruth's?

The Pressure to Join Up

Rose　Like little boys, aren't they? Off on a big adventure.

SCENE 2

Read　　In 1914, men were not afraid to join up. They had no idea what the war would be like. Newspapers promised that it would be over by Christmas.

Young men remembered the adventure stories and poems of their childhood in which men were heroes doing daring deeds. Their friends were 'comrades', the enemy was referred to as 'the foe' and the dead were described as 'the fallen'. The real hardships of war were never explored. An entry in the personal column of The Times (Summer 1914) is typical of this spirit.

> PAULINE – Alas, it cannot be. But I will dash into the great venture with all that pride and spirit an ancient race has given me.

Women were used as part of the propaganda of war to encourage young men, like Sidney and Tommy in the play, to join up.

Oh we don't want to lose you,

But we think you ought to go;

For your king and your country

Both need you so.

We shall want you and miss you,

Bu with all our might and main

We will thank you, cheer you, kiss you,

When you come back again.

None but the Brave deserve the Fair.

TO THE YOUNG WOMEN OF LONDON

Is your "Best Boy" wearing Khaki? If not don't **YOU** **THINK** he should be?

If he does not think that you and your country are worth fighting for—do you think he is **WORTHY** of you?

Don't pity the girl who is alone—her young man is probably a soldier—fighting for her and her country—and for **YOU**.

If your young man neglects his duty to his King and Country, the time may come when he will **NEGLECT YOU**.

Think it over—then ask him to

JOIN THE ARMY TO-DAY

Your King and Country Need You.

Will you answer your Country's Call? Each day is fraught with the gravest possibilities, and at this very moment the Empire is on the brink of the greatest war in the history of the world.

In this crisis your Country calls on all her young unmarried men to rally round the Flag and enlist in the ranks of her Army.

If every patriotic young man answers her call, England and her Empire will emerge stronger and more united than ever.

If you are unmarried and between 18 and 30 years old will you answer your Country's Call? and go to the nearest Recruiter ... whose address you can get at any Post Office, and

JOIN THE ARMY TO-DAY!

5 QUESTIONS TO MEN WHO HAVE *NOT* ENLISTED

1. If you are physically fit and between 19 and 38 years of age, are you really satisfied with what you are doing to-day **?**

2. Do you feel happy as you walk along the streets and see other men wearing the King's uniform **?**

3. What will you say in years to come when people ask you—"Where did you serve in the great War" **?**

4. What will you answer when your children grow up, and say "Father, why weren't you a soldier, too" **?**

5. What would happen to the Empire if every man stayed at home **?**

YOUR KING AND COUNTRY NEED YOU ENLIST TO-DAY

GOD SAVE THE KING.

Talk Imagine you are Dorothy. Sid has not yet enlisted. What would your thoughts be about the possibility of him going off to war? What would you say to him?

1 In pairs, act out a dialogue between you and Sid. Try and bring out the feelings of the characters as well as their sense of duty and responses to propaganda. Decide where to set it – in the kitchen, on a walk, in the pub, or wherever you choose.

2 Write out your dialogue as a script.

Read Compare these two descriptions of joining up.

There was such a rush for fellows to go in the Army that they'd had to get quite a number of officers in to deal with all these recruits. Even so, it was about two hours before my turn came. I was only eighteen and I didn't weigh very much – I didn't look very much like a soldier – I weighed 8 stone 11 lb, but I was passed. I was given a parcel of food and a railway warrant and we were taken down to Midland station and put on a train and instructed to report to the officer at Newhaven.

Anyway when we got down to Newhaven it was between nine and ten and a party of soldiers came to meet us, and we were taken up what seemed to me to be miles, up a long valley from the railway station. It was pitch dark and we didn't know where we were going. Anyway we got to a place where there seemed to be a lot of tents and we were taken into a great big one, a marquee, with a long table down the middle and some forms and we were sat down and presently two fellows came with a big basketful of loaves which had been cut in two and another two men came down with a big dixie full of herrings and they plonked one of these herrings on half a loaf of bread and slapped the other half on the top of it and that was my supper.

As far as I could see in the night there must have been hundreds of tents and the Sergeant counted us out, there was twelve men put into each tent and he shoved us in. He said, 'There's some blankets there.' There was nothing on the floor, just the bare soil, and so we got down as best we could.

About six o'clock the next morning there was such a noise outside and then a fellow blew a trumpet and I had a feeling that must have been the Reveille. We got up. None of us had bothered about undressing. Some Sergeants came up then, 'Come on, fall in!' We didn't know what it was we'd got to fall into. It might have been the sea for all *we* knew!

Gunner R. Elwis, Royal Garrison Artillery

I never said anything about enlisting when I went home that night and on the Sunday morning there was an OHMS envelope. I didn't open it. So when breakfast started Mother said, 'What's that? Get it opened.' I didn't want to open it but she insisted. The instructions were to report to the Drill Hall, Grange Road, Middlesborough. When I read that out, 'Jack,' she said to Dad, 'stop his gallop. He doesn't go! There's lots that will go before that boy goes.' So Dad said, 'Have you joined, Pete?' I said, 'Yes, Dad.' 'Well,' he said, 'this is a nice how-do-you-do.'
Then Mother started to get excited. She said, 'Stop his gallop, Dad. You see Chief Constable Riches. He's not going.' So Dad said, 'Well, just supposing, Pete, you came back with a leg or arm off? Who wants you?' I said, 'Let me get there first, Dad, before I get back.' 'So,' he said, 'It's alright you talking like that but you don't know what you've done.' I said, 'But I do know what I've done.' 'Alright,' he said, 'if you've made your bed, you'll have to lie in it.' I said, 'I'll lie in it, Dad.' 'Well,' he said to Mother, 'there's no more to be said, Polly.' And that was the start.

Trooper P. Mason, West Yorkshire Regiment

Talk   1   How much do you think these two men knew about what they were doing? What evidence is there for this?

2   How much do you think Tommy and Sid knew what they were doing at the start of the play, when they enlisted? Explain your answer.

Read

> **Ted**   If I was your age I expect I'd be off along with you, running down the road as fast as my legs would carry me. All those lads in uniform. It's a fine thing to be a soldier . . .

SCENE 1

Compare what Ted says with what the writer D.H. Lawrence wrote in a letter at this time.

I know that, for me, the war is wrong. I know that if the Germans wanted my little house, I would rather give it to them than fight for it: because my little house is not important enough to me. If another man must fight for his house, the more's the pity. But it is his affair. To fight for possessions, goods, is what the soul will not do.

Talk   1   Which of these two views do you agree with?

2   Do you think fighting is ever justified?

3   Would you defend your country if asked to?

4   Would you have joined up with Tommy and Sid?

THE WAR: 1914–18

"Women's Work"

> **Vera** The war's not just abroad . . . The women of Britain must learn to fight the war at home.

SCENE 8

Read Study these two accounts and the photographs which follow them.

I worked at Woolwich dockyard during the First World War. I started work when I left school at fourteen. That was 1917, the year before the war ended. We were in what they called the propaganda part. We were doing leaflets. They were all printed in German and we had to pack them in bulk and then we had a yellow cord, and we had to put them through this yellow cord and they were taken by our airmen and dropped over Germany.

In 1918, when the war ended, we all went down to the waters edge and we went mad. After the war ended, they kept us on for a little while and they brought us the compasses that the men used to use. We used to scrape the mud off them and some were all bloodstained and we had to get them all cleaned to go back to the stores.

Mrs. Jones

During the First World War, I was in the gunpowder shed at Abbey Wood, filling the cordite bags that go in the back of the shells. I volunteered to work there to help with the war. I earned good money there, about £3 a week. The bags were made of serge. They were cream and red, and had five holes in them which you filled with gunpowder and then stitched along the top. The powder came in little silver jars, and we had a silver shovel to get it out. The powder would be brought to us so we wouldn't be kept waiting, since we were on piece work. I would write down how many I'd done for the day, so I knew how much money I was to get.

It was such good money that I didn't want to leave, but then the shed next to us got blown up. Some of the girls were blinded, and some were injured, and my dad said he'd rather have no money and have me safe.

Beverley Langford

Talk

1 What other jobs can you think of that women would be likely to have taken over during the war? List them.

2 What jobs are done by the female characters in *A Kiss From France*?

3 When Sid comes home on leave he remarks that 'A woman without a man spells trouble'. What do you think he means by this?

4 In his absence Dorothy has arranged to put new shelves up in the shop. What is his attitude to this? What does this tell us about him?

5 How do you think Dorothy is affected by her new job? Choose details from the play to support your answer.

6 List all the ways in which you think relationships between men and women might have changed as a result of the new experiences and jobs open to women. Which of these do you consider most important and why?

Women and Relationships

Read   Although there is plenty of material describing the horrors of life in the trenches, there is comparatively little published information about the suffering of women at home. In these diary extracts, Vera Brittain describes some of these pressures.

April 19th 1915

I had another violent fit of desperation this morning. I suppose I must get used to them, but they alarm me a little and make me wonder what I may do if Roland [her boyfriend] dies. At present my one desire in life is to see him again. I think how little there is of any tendency for the war to end, of how he is in the trenches day in and day out in momently danger, of the long long weary months ahead, & I wonder how I shall ever bear them and get through them without any light, anything to look forward to, to carry me along. O glorious time of youth indeed! This is part of my life when I ought to be living every moment to the full, tasting the sweetness of every joy, full of love and life and aspiration and hope, exulting in my own existence. Instead, I can only think how weary are the heavy hours, wonder how I can get through their aching suspense, wonder when they will end — and how. Ah! those who are old and think this war so terrible do not know what it means to us who are young. They at least have had their joy, have it now to think of and look back on; for us the chief part of our lives, the part which makes all the rest worth while, has either never dawned, or else we have for a moment seen what is possible only to have it snatched from our eyes.

April 25th

. . . I wrote a long letter between lunch and tea, telling him of my desire to nurse, of my wish that he should tell me of the horrors he sees because 'women are no longer the sheltered darlings of men's playtime, fit only for the nursery or the drawing-room.'

August 5

. . . I received a letter from him before I went back to the Hospital this evening . . . 'I used to talk about the Beauty of War, but it is only War in the abstract that is beautiful. Modern warfare is merely a trade, and it is only a matter of taste whether one is a soldier or a greengrocer, as far as I can see. Sometimes by dint of an opportunity a single man may rise from the sordidness to a deed of beauty: that is all.'

September 27 1915

It has been a dreadful day — waiting and waiting and able to settle nothing. Ah! a year of war has taught me what these victories mean, though we certainly haven't had much experience of victory. At first it is all splendour and glory and advance and captures and wonderful achievements. And then gradually comes admissions of hardly-earned triumphs being won back by the enemy, stories of horror which the papers dare not print on their principal pages, and long, long casualty lists in which each name means a home rendered desolate.

January 13 1916

I arrived at a very opportune though very awful moment. All R's things had just been sent back from the front and they were all lying on the floor. I had no idea before of the aftermath of an officer's death, or what the returned kit, about which so many letters have been written in the papers really meant. It was terrible. Mrs Leighton and Clare were both crying as bitterly as on the day we heard of his death. There were his clothes — the clothes in which he came home from the front last time — another set rather less worn, and underclothing and accessories of various descriptions. Everything was damp and worn and simply caked with mud. All the sepulchres and catacombs of Rome could not make me realise mortality and decay and corruption as vividly as did the smell of those clothes. I know now what he meant when he used to write 'this refuse-heap of a country' or 'a trench that is nothing but a charnel-house'. The only things untouched by damp or mud or mould were my photographs, kept carefully in an envelope, and his leather cigarette case, with a few cigarettes, a tiny photo of his Mother & George Meredith . . . There was his haversack crammed full of letters . . . Mrs Leighton remarked almost with awe how very openly one has to live at the Front, when any moment one's most private personal belongings become the property of one's nearest relations and friends.

Talk
1 Describe the different moods you can detect in these entries.
2 What do you think Vera Brittain's own views about the war are? Use the diary extracts to support your case.
3 Re-read the scenes in *A Kiss From France* in which Dorothy appears or is mentioned. What different moods do you imagine her going through? List these.

Assignment
Write a series of diary extracts for Dorothy.

Stage 1 Decide which period of the play you are going to concentrate on.

Stage 2 Make a list of the significant events for Dorothy during this period.

Stage 3 Make a rough draft.

You could use Vera Brittain's style as a model for Dorothy's diary if you wish, or you could research other diaries of this period to help you.

Life at the Front

Read   Study these photographs and read this description of a British attack on the German trenches.

It was not a good start. Up the road out of Fricourt, a dead major lay with his eyes open; they were very blue and his arm was flung out as if pointing the way. We moved to the right and past some more unburied dead. One had died of haemorrhage with red froth round his lips; he looked like a clown. Then we found our jumping off place, more like a gully than a trench. I looked over the top: there was a small copse, I noticed, to the left. I extended my men along the gully and looked at my synchronised watch.

Nothing happened at first. We advanced at a slow double. I noticed that it had begun to rain. Then the enemy machine-gunning started, first one gun, then many. They traversed, and every now and then came the swish of bullets. Someone on the extreme right fell.

Long gave the command to lie down, and my men took it for a signal for themselves too. There for a while we stuck. The rain continued and the machine-gunning too. We lay as flat as possible and winced each time the machine-gun bullets passed. There were one or two groans; men were getting hit.

It's a bloody death trap, someone said. I told him to shut up. But was he right? More men were getting wounded. A shell landed just in front of me, dislodging a sapling, which fell across my legs, but failing to explode. I felt temporarily elated at the escape. But what was happening – had the order to retire failed to reach me? But I couldn't retire without orders.

Talk

1 Describe your own impressions of what you have seen and read.

2 Select two speeches from *A Kiss From France:*
   a) one that reflects the horror of the fighting;
   b) one that shows it in a more patriotic light.

Read

Compare Sidney's speech in Scene 11 of the play with this description of a day's bombardment.

18 December 1914

The show started with an artillery bombardment – you never heard such a din. The enormous howitzer shells (our own) came over our heads, plainly visible in the sky, and burst with a deafening report just in front of us. Incidentally they wiped out dozens of our own men. One fell in one of our trenches and killed thirteen.

Then I opened fire on a house at 200 yards range and my second shot blew it to bits. About 30 Germans ran out of it and were, I believe, shot by our Infantry.

At 2.20 the bombardment abruptly ceased and the infantry advanced. When they arrived at the edge of the wood they were met by a perfect hail of bullets. I had an exciting run over to the officer commanding the front trenches. One man was shot through the head only a few yards off me and one or two of the others badly wounded.

Meanwhile the stretcher bearers were bringing in the wounded. They came from the front, right over the parapet where I was sitting and they seemed quite oblivious of danger from the flying bullets. An officer was brought in shot through the lung and another officer was killed just in front of us. This went on till 4 p.m. and then it began to get dark, and the scene when darkness fell will live in my memory forever, I think.

There was a steady stream of wounded all through the night and it was a horrible sight seeing these poor fellows brought in covered from head to toe with mud. Some could walk with help and they all had to go down these horrible plank roads in the dark, tripping and stumbling and often falling into the mud.

At about 6 p.m. I found the Major and we left the dismal scene and went back to General Headquarters. What a very different aspect everything had, back there! The General and his Staff sitting round a table with maps and plans seemed infinitely far away from that horrible wood.

The Major and I were kept waiting for over an hour but eventually got our orders – which incidentally did not please us very much – and returned to the wood and started looking for the guns.

It was pitch dark and, after stumbling about in the sea of mud by the light of the Major's torch for an hour or so, we got absolutely lost.

We decided to separate then, and we wandered and wandered about in that infernal forest most of the night. I fell into trenches full of water and now and then came up against a barbed wire entanglement with a sentry on the other side telling me to put my 'hands up', fortunately he did not shoot. By 1 a.m. I was completely done, and if a Jack Johnson or other missile had come along and knocked me down I should have said Thank You.

I am glad to have seen war from the point of view of the Infantry. It was an experience that Gunners don't usually have. As I came back covered from head to foot in mud I passed the Artillery position. Some very smart RFA Officers had just done stables and looked wonderingly at me as if surprised that anyone with a gun badge in his cap should have the face to turn out so badly dressed, and so unwashed and unshaved. And I have seen the Artillery hit our own Infantry when I was in the Infantry position. I heard one poor wretch say 'I have three wounds and two are by our own artillery', and it made me think a good deal.

Captain Maurice Mascall, Royal Garrison Artillery.

Talk

1 Describe in detail how the war affected Sidney.

2 How do you think the writer of the last extract, Captain Mascall, was affected?

3 List the similarities and differences in their experiences and their reactions.

Assignment

Write a speech based on Captain Mascall's diary extract, in which he, like Sidney, describes his memories of a particularly horrific day.

War-Wounded

Read   Men wounded in the fighting were either placed in Field Hospitals in France or sent back home. In this extract Siegfried Sassoon, who suffered badly from shell-shock, describes the different types of visitors he received while in a London Hospital.

> Some Senior Officer Under Whom I'd Served – Modest, politely subordinate, strongly imbued with the 'spirit of the Regiment' and quite ready to go out again. 'Awfully nice of you to come and see me, sir.' Feeling that I ought to jump out of bed and salute, and that it would be appropriate and pleasant to introduce him to 'some of my people' (preferably of impeccable social status). Willingness to discuss active service technicalities and revive memories of shared front-line experience.
>
> Middle-Aged Or Elderly Male Civilian – tendency (in response to sympathetic gratitude for services rendered to King and Country) to assume haggard facial aspect of one who had 'been through hell'. Inclination to wish that my wound was a bit worse than it actually was, and have nurses hovering round with discreet reminders that my strength mustn't be overtaxed. Inability to reveal anything crudely horrifying to civilian sensibilities. 'Oh yes, I'll be out there again by the autumn.' (Grimly wan reply to suggestions that I was now honourably qualified for a home service job.) Secret antagonism to all uncomplimentary references to the German Army.
>
> Charming Sister Of Brother Officer – Jocular, talkative, debonair, and diffidently heroic. Wishful to be wearing all possible medal-ribbons on pyjama jacket. Able to furnish a bright account of her brother (if still at front) and suppressing all unpalatable facts about the war. 'Jolly decent of you to blow in and see me.'

Talk   1   In your own words describe the three different types of visitors he received.

2   What are Sassoon's different reactions to each of them? Why does he react in these ways?

Assignment   In fours, make up a scene in which a wounded soldier is visited by three different characters. These could be the ones suggested by Sassoon or they could be made up by the group.

Stage 1   Decide what your wounded soldier's attitude to the characters will be.

Stage 2   Decide what his visitors think about the war.

Stage 3   Act out your scene.

Stage 4   Write out your scene as a script with appropriate stage directions.

The Death of Tommy

Sidney   Tommy was writhing about, trying to put the fire out. Then he began to go off like a firework. The fire was exploding the cartridges in his belt . . . It was the most horrible thing I've ever seen.

SCENE 11

Read   In the play, Tommy's mother receives a letter like this, telling her that he has been killed.

60th Field Ambulance,
France.
October 30th, 1915.

Dear Mr Bailey,

It is with the deepest regret and sorrow that I write to sympathise with you upon the death of your son.

It was my painful duty to conduct the burial service yesterday. It was a sad blow to the whole of his Company when they heard that he had been killed for he was deservedly popular with everybody. His real Christian influence will be greatly missed.

I had come to know him as a real friend and it was always a pleasure to chat with him and to have him at our services.

Your sorrow will be very deep. But I pray that the heavy weight of sorrow may be eased by the knowledge that he was a true Christian and a true soldier and such sacrifice as his has made us all the nobler. You will meet him again when all tears shall be wiped away.

God bless you all.

I am,
Yours sincerely,
C.E. James (Wesleyan Chaplain).

Assignment   Imagine that you have been given the job of writing to Tommy's mother, telling her of her son's death.

Stage 1   Decide what you want to say about Tommy.
Stage 2   Decide what you want to say about the way in which he died.
Stage 3   Make a rough draft.
Stage 4   Now write the letter.

Read   As the war progressed, bad news such as this became more and more common. Study the reactions to such news, as described below by Arnold Toynbee.

> In 1915, soon after I left Oxford for London to do war-work there, I was sent on some errand to the War Office in Whitehall. As I was entering, I saw, facing me, a notice-board on which there was posted a list of officers recently reported killed and, at the same moment, two women passed me. They had just read on the board the announcement of a death. One of the two was weeping bitterly; the other was talking rapidly and emphatically – as if her hurrying words could overtake and perhaps retrieve the cruel loss that had been suffered by her companion. I can see those two poor women's faces as clearly in my mind's eye as, on that day, I saw them in the life.

Talk   1   Make up a scene, set in 1915, in which the news of a death is learned.

> **Stage 1**   Decide who has been killed and the relationships between the other people in the scene.
>
> **Stage 2**   Decide on their reactions to the news and on how they would show this.
>
> **Stage 3**   Decide to what extent the news of growing casualties in France is starting to make those at home question the point of the war.

Conscientious Objectors

Read   For the first year and a half of the war, enlisting to fight was voluntary. However, with growing casualties there were not enough men coming forward. In May 1916 conscription was enforced. This meant that all able-bodied men between the ages of 18 and 30 could be called up to fight.

Some men did not wish to fight. For some this was because of their religious beliefs or because they were pacifists; others simply did not want to die. Those who refused to fight because of a strongly held belief were called conscientious objectors.

Conscientious objectors had to appear before a tribunal. Between 16000 and 20000 men took their cases to be judged in this way and about 10000 were successful. If a tribunal did not accept the reasons given, objectors were often imprisoned.

In the following extract from a novel set at this time, a young man, Lucas, experiences an unsympathetic hearing.

> The direct question made Lucas start. With some difficulty he got out: 'Eighteen.'
> 'Much too young to have settled opinions. All the same these youngsters, changing their minds every two minutes. Hmm!' He picked up a pencil, made a small circle on the paper before him and scored it through. 'I really don't see

why we are supposed to deal with a case of this sort. We have enough problems as it is.' He sounded peevish.

'We ought in all fairness to let the fellow state his case, Mr Chairman.' The Rev. Blenkinsop fingered his dog-collar. 'He is here inescapably. Justice must be seen to be done. You do agree?.'

Port-wine red, the chairman scooped up his papers, tapped them together, laid them in an even neater pile and finally agreed. 'Very well, very well.' He glared at Lucas. 'Speak up then. Religious objections?'

'No.'

'No *sir*!'

'No sir,' Lucas croaked, his jaw suddenly cramped and rigid from the nightmare absurdity of what was happening.

'Get on with it, we haven't all day! Explain yourself.'

Lucas wetted his lips with the tip of his tongue. 'It's like this see . . .' His voice was no more than a whisper.

'Don't mumble in your boots!'

'LIKE THIS,' Lucas said, bold now as resentment hit him, but scaring himself by the booming of his own voice. 'We gets born by no choosing; no wishing to be. But now we *are* born the life we've got is a kind of treasure. The way I sees it, nobody's got the right to take away this treasure from another person, even if he is a Hun. After all we're all people. What's the point in slaughtering each other?' He looked along the row of tight well-fed faces, hoping for something . . . anything that might show a hint of under-standing or fellow-feeling. The stone-wall eyes stared flintily back. He went on doggedly: 'Don't you see? Life ain't somethink to be treated like an old paper bag, screwed up and chucked into the gutter without a second thought. It's a . . . a diamond. A precious thing we should care for and respect.' Oh Gawd, they thought he was crackers. Row of suet dumplings. Useless, useless – but he must go on though it would be an agony. Go on, go on! Before the chance was lost forever and he was left to kick himself from now till doomsday.

'Totally irrelevant!' The chairman intervened. 'No point in listening to any more. If you can't produce a better reason than this garbled nonsense then your case is closed.'

'But I haven't finished,' Lucas said desperately. 'You must hear it all. Justice must be seen to be done. *He* said that,' pointing at the clergyman.

'Impudent puppy . . .' the chairman began, but didn't continue, leaving a small wordless space which Lucas seized before he could be interrupted again.

'If you looks . . . really looks I mean, not like most people who go around with their eyes shut . . . if you really looks at the world, there's so much beauty – and a lot of ugliness I grant you – but the beauty's there and that's the important thing. I reckon that's what it's all about. Beauty. Looking at it and trying to make it in whatever way is right for you. The war ain't any kind of beauty. It's ugly and wasteful. What right have I, or you – anybody, to go round killing and killing. There ain't no worse sin and

I can't . . . *won't* take part.' He looked at the floor wishing Bella was there to hear. Perhaps she might then have understood. 'That's all I have to say.'

His words seemed suspended in the air for seconds after he had finished speaking. A strange confusing silence reigned as if his cheek in being there, let alone in concocting such a statement, had temporarily taken the wind out of their sails. It was the woman who recovered first. She craned her long neck towards him.

'Tell me, young man, do you eat cheese?'

Lucas stared, baffled. 'Yes, ma'm.'

'Then I put it to you that you are showing every sign of being a hypocrite. To eat cheese means you take part in the killing of those maggots whose job it is to provide you with the cheese. You cannot accept one kind of killing and reject another.'

The logic and truth of this was quite beyond him, but the petty stupidity was not. He felt outraged. 'I was speaking of human life, ma'am. Maggots make a meal of us all soon enough. I ain't going to provide 'em with extra rations just at present.'

The chairman rose to his feet, spluttering. Through the turmoil in his mind Lucas caught the words, 'Heard enough . . . not even British . . .' and the final judgement, 'Objection overruled.'

Talk

1   List all the arguments used by Lucas in this extract.

2   Which of the arguments do you find most compelling?

3   How fair is this tribunal? Do you side with it, or with Lucas? Give your reasons.

Read

Various methods of persuasion were used to change the minds of conscientious objectors.

Some of the early batches . . . were taken singly and run across the yard to special rooms – airy enough but from which they could see nothing. They were fed on bread and water and some of them presently came round. I had them placed in special rooms, nude, but with their full army kit on the floor for them to put on as soon as they were so minded. There were no blankets or substitutes for clothing left in the rooms which were quite bare. Several of the men held out naked for several hours but they gradually accepted the inevitable. Forty of the conscientious objectors who passed through my hands are now quite willing soldiers.

Lt-Col Reginald Brooke, Commander of the Military Detention Barracks, Wandsworth. Daily Express, *4 July 1916*

Assignment

Stage 1   Consider these questions.

a) Re-read Albert Warren's speech which begins Scene 9. What are his reasons for not wanting to fight?

     b) Which of the characters in the play feels that Albert should be fighting?

     c) Which of the characters has some sympathy with Albert? How is this shown?

     d) What would you have done in Albert's situation? Would you have gone to war?

Stage 2   Choose three characters from the play, including Albert. Add one more to represent your own views. Make up a suitable name for her/him.

Stage 3   Plan a situation in which these characters could meet and become involved in a discussion or argument with Albert. You might wish to make this start with a dramatic incident, for example Vera storming into Dorothy's shop, telling her she was going to stand outside preventing customers from shopping where cowards were employed.

Stage 4   Write out your scene as a short story.

The Characters in the Play

Talk   1   In groups of four, divide up the eight characters in the play so that each person decides on two characters to study.

2   Give each person in your group a letter, A B C or D.

3   Re-group so that all the As can work together in a larger group. Do the same for the Bs, Cs and Ds.

4   Make notes:
     a) on what the most significant events in the play were for your two characters
     b) on your assessment of the kind of people your characters are.

5   Return to your first group of four and report your findings back to them.

6   Listen to comments about the six characters you did not choose, and make notes on at least one of them.

Assignment   Choose three characters from *A Kiss From France*. Describe their experience of the war. Include the following:
a) what you feel to be the main features of their characters
b) reference to the play and quotations from it where these are helpful
c) your own reactions to these characters
d) an indication of which character you feel most close to.
You could put yourself in the place of the three characters, and write in the first person.

AFTER THE WAR

Changing Roles for Women

Read After the war there were over a million women in full-time employment. Before the war middle and upper-class women had rarely worked except in jobs such as teaching or nursing. During the war women took over jobs previously done by men and were employed in banking, plumbing, engineering, farming, gravedigging etc. Study this table.

Women employed in Britain	1914	1918
Metal industries	170 000	594 000
Chemical industry	40 000	104 000
Food, drink & tobacco	196 000	235 000
Government establishments	2000	225 000
Wood industries	44 000	79 000

Talk 1 Describe the ways in which the women in *A Kiss From France* coped and found greater independence during the war.

2 Decide which of the women in the play became most independent as a result of the war. Explain your choice.

Read

My husband only got home after the end of the war and he was so ill. Malaria. He was in the Scottish Horse and he'd been in Gallipoli and Egypt. I hadn't seen him for four years. My little girl was three and a bit and he'd never seen her. He came home straight off a hospital ship and he was so weary and unwell he went straight to bed. I said to Connie, 'Go in and see your Daddy.' She was very shy of him, but she went and stood at the bedroom door. I said, 'Well, say something to Daddy.' She said, 'My Mummy's made scones for you.' He just looked at her. He was too ill, too tired to speak. We lived with my family for a while. We'd had a war wedding before he left, so we didn't have a house of our own. After a few months we were given a railway carriage to live in. That was the Home for Heroes. It was the best they could do. So we started our married life in a converted railway carriage.

Mrs I. McNicol

> Us fellows, it took us years to get over it. Years! Long after when you were working, married, had kids, you'd be lying in bed with your wife and you'd see it all before you. Couldn't sleep. Couldn't lie still. Many's and many's the time I've got up and tramped the streets till it came daylight. Walking, walking – anything to get away from your thoughts. And many's the time I've met other fellows that were out there doing exactly the same thing. That went on for years, that did.
>
> *Rifleman Fred White, King's Royal Rifle Corps*

Talk

1 How did the war change the lives of Mrs. McNichol's husband and of Fred White?

2 How does Rose Griffiths change during the play? To help you decide this, make a list of all you know about her at the beginning of the play and at the end of it.

3 How are the other characters changed by the war? In pairs, describe the main changes in each of the characters.

Assignment

Stage 1 Choose the characters in the play you have found most interesting.

Stage 2 Describe your characters with particular emphasis on ways in which they change during the play.

Stage 3 Write helpful notes for actors about to play the characters.

Stage 4 Decide on an appropriate format for presenting your work.

The Ending

Talk

1 Re-read the speech Tommy makes at the end of the play. What does being a hero mean to Tommy? What does it mean to you?

2 What do you think would have happened to the characters in the play after the war ended?

Assignment

Write two additional scenes for the play, one set in 1919 and the other set ten years later.

THE PLAY IN PERFORMANCE

Some Key Techniques

Tableau

A silent group of actors arranged to represent a scene.

This can be used to great effect in *A Kiss From France* e.g. at the start of the play where the audience sees Sidney going through the pockets of Tommy, who is dead.

Task   Make a list of the other tableaux in the play and say what effect you think they have.

Monologue

A long speech by one person.

This allows characters to speak with an honesty, directness and degree of detail not normally possible in a dialogue. Characters speaking in monologue are really speaking their private thoughts out loud.

Task   Turn Scene 2 into a monologue for Dorothy or Rose.

Music

Music is often used in plays but in *A Kiss From France* it has been deliberately chosen to set atmosphere and to provoke thought.

Task   Listen to the beginning of Fauré's Requiem. What effect does it produce at the start of the play?

Design

Choose three scenes from the play and draw diagrams of the sets you would use if you were directing them.

Mark in your characters' movements on the diagrams.

Make a list of any props your characters would need.

ADDITIONAL ASSIGNMENTS

1 Imagine you are one of these characters still alive today, in your nineties. One of your great grandchildren is doing a project about World War One.

   Tell your great grandchild some of your memories of World War One. Work in pairs, each imagining you are the great-grandparent. Tape your conversations.

2 Write a series of about six letters that you imagine might have been sent between Dorothy and Sid. Try to show:
   a) Sid's first impressions;
   b) his feelings for Dorothy;
   c) his discovery of what war is really like;
   d) his state of mind after experiencing the full horror of fighting;
   e) Dorothy's feelings for Sid;
   f) her feelings about the war;
   g) her changing life at home;
   h) her responses to Sid's letters.

3 Write an essay about attitudes to war.

   Stage 1 Do some research into other wars e.g. World War Two, The Korean and Vietnam wars, The Falklands War, the conflicts in Beirut and Ulster.
   Stage 2 Decide what associations the words *patriotic* and *heroic* can have and in what ways they can be used.
   Stage 3 Make a rough draft, presenting your own views on war as well as your reactions to the opinions you have come across in your research.

4 Prepare a programme for a production of *A Kiss From France*. Include:
   a) a brief summary of the play;
   b) notes on characters;
   c) notes on key themes.

5 Write a monologue for a character in the play who is not given this particular kind of speech.

6 Do some research into the songs and music of World War One. Write an essay, based on what you find. Include:
   a) a brief description of what they were about;
   b) the feelings they chose to decribe;
   c) your assessment of the mood they appear to have been trying to encourage.

You could do the same for the poetry of World War One.